Meeting special needs

A practical guide to support children with Epilepsy

by Rachel Baker

This booklet is dedicated to
Sonny Baker-Taylor
for his boundless energy,
strength and smile.

In this book the use of he, him or his is gender neutral and is
intended to include both sexes.

Published by Step Forward Publishing Limited
St Jude's Church, Dulwich Road, Herne Hill, London, SE24 0PB Tel. 020 7738 5454
© Step Forward Publishing Limited 2007 www.practicalpreschool.com

Meeting special needs. A practical guide to support children with Epilepsy ISBN: 978-1-904-575-11-5

Contents

Pages to copy and use:

Epilepsy is covered by the Disability Discrimination Act (2001), which means that no child can be refused a place at school or nursery due to their condition.

What is Epilepsy?

Epilepsy is the most common serious neurological condition in the UK, and affects one in every 131 people.

The term 'epilepsy' is used to describe recurrent seizures, and comes from the Greek word meaning 'to take hold of, or seize'.

A seizure can be described as a short-circuit in the brain, which triggers an electrical storm, resulting in a loss of control depending on which part of the brain is affected.

Neurons transmit electrical messages between one another and if there is chemical imbalance, these messages are all triggered at once, causing a seizure. The effect on the body depends on where the disturbance occurs in the brain.

The brain is divided into two halves or *hemispheres*, with four *lobes* in each. Each of these controls a different part of the body. Each hemisphere controls the opposite side of the body, which is why an injury on one side of the brain affects the opposite side of the body.

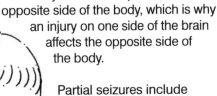

Partial seizures include 'milder' cases of epilepsy, which can be as simple as a funny taste in the mouth, or the jerking of one limb. Sometimes these can be a warning that a more serious seizure is about to occur, and are known as 'auras'. In most cases, children who suffer from partial seizures do not lose consciousness, though they may become confused or disorientated.

Generalised seizures can be much more alarming for carers, as the child will lose consciousness, and is at greater risk of injury.

> There are over 40 seizure types which come under two main categories: partial and generalised.
>
> Partial seizures only affect part of the brain, whereas generalised seizures affect the whole brain.

Partial seizures

Simple partial seizures
(focal cortical seizures)

The child will not lose consciousness during the seizure but will lose control of certain body movements. The child's senses may be distorted causing him to see, hear, or smell things that are not there.

They may also experience unusual feelings. The child will usually be able to talk and answer questions during the seizure and will most likely remember what has occurred after the seizure. **Simple partial seizures typically last two to ten seconds, but may last longer.**

Complex partial seizures
(psychomotor or temporal lobe seizures)

The degree of consciousness during these seizures depends on the child. During the seizure he may stop, stare and will become unaware of what is happening around him. He may produce inappropriate behaviour (tapping the desk, picking at his clothes, making chewing movements or wandering around).

After the seizure the child will probably be confused and disorientated. **Complex partial seizures typically last two to four minutes.**

Generalised seizures

Tonic-clonic seizures *(formerly grand mal)*

During a tonic-clonic seizure the child will suddenly become stiff, lose consciousness and fall to the floor (tonic phase). He may let out a loud cry as the muscles in the chest and larynx contract, and as the air rushes between the vocal chords a sound is made.

Don't panic, as this cry does not mean that the child is in pain. His limbs will then begin to jerk rhythmically (the clonic phase). It's quite normal for a child to become incontinent during this type of seizure and he may bite his tongue, which can cause bleeding. However, never put anything in the mouth to prevent this.

Saliva that has not been swallowed during the seizure may froth at the mouth and breathing can become irregular, sometimes leading to the child turning blue at the lips. If the seizure is within their 'normal' time limit, don't panic.

The diagram below shows the placement of each lobe,
and possible symptoms of epileptic activity in each area:

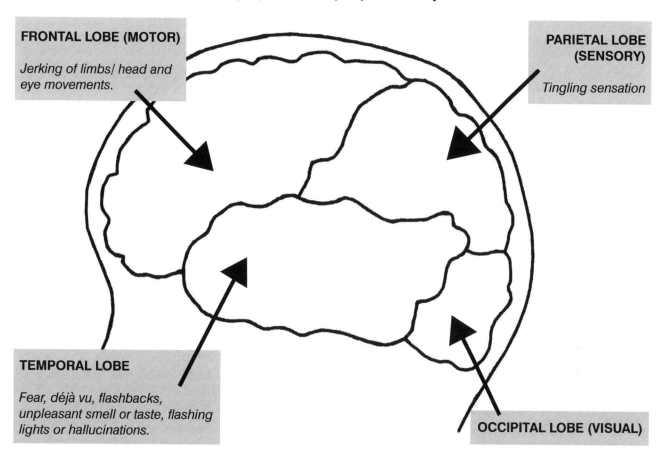

FRONTAL LOBE (MOTOR)

*Jerking of limbs/ head and
eye movements.*

**PARIETAL LOBE
(SENSORY)**

Tingling sensation

TEMPORAL LOBE

*Fear, déjà vu, flashbacks,
unpleasant smell or taste, flashing
lights or hallucinations.*

OCCIPITAL LOBE (VISUAL)

**A tonic-clonic seizure generally lasts for one to three
minutes, but if it lasts longer than five minutes or the
child has two in a row without recovering in between,
medical attention is required.**

Absence seizure *(formerly petit mal)*

During the seizure the child will lose awareness for
a few seconds and will look as if he is daydreaming.
Because these seizures are brief and subtle they
may be difficult to recognize. Therefore absence
seizures are usually not diagnosed until many
have occurred.

All staff should be made aware of these seizures
so that they know the child is not just daydreaming.
Because these seizures may occur many times a day,
they are likely to interfere with the child's ability to
absorb information.

The child will be unaware of these seizures when they
occur and therefore will need to be told what he has
missed, once he regains awareness.

Myoclonic seizures

'Myo' means muscle and a myoclonic seizure is a brief
jerk of a group of muscles. It looks as if the child has
just been shocked. People who do not have epilepsy
may experience a jerk like this while falling asleep.

Myoclonic seizures in epilepsy involve sudden
jerks of the arms, shoulders, neck, body, or legs,
affecting both sides at the same time, which may
result in the person falling. These seizures usually
begin in childhood and are often a part of a pattern of
epilepsy that may also include other types
of seizures.

Atonic seizures

'Atonic' means
without tone. In
these seizures the
muscles lose all
strength, instead of
becoming stiff. The
person remains
conscious but may
fall to the ground
without warning.

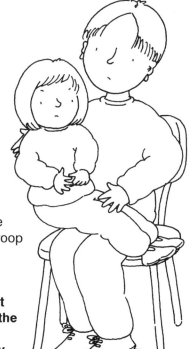

In a milder form, the
child's head may droop
or he may
drop things.

**These seizures last
only seconds and the
child will recover
almost immediately.**

What causes epilepsy?

Epilepsy can be developed as the result of a brain injury, stroke or an infection such as meningitis. Where there is a known cause, the condition is called 'symptomatic', and where there is no known cause it's referred to as 'idiopathic' epilepsy. 'Cryptogenic' epilepsy is where a cause hasn't yet been found, but one is suspected.

Children who are not born with the condition, but later develop idiopathic epilepsy have the greatest chance of 'growing out' of it. About 70% of all children will eventually grow out of it, but these tend to be children whose epilepsy is easy to control. If a child has been fit-free for two years, their physician will wean them off their medication and monitor them to see if their seizures re-occur.

How is epilepsy diagnosed?

Anyone can develop epilepsy at any time, but in most instances people develop epilepsy in their early years. Once seizures occur, tests are taken to make sure that the fits are not caused by fever (febrile convulsion), or by a lack of certain minerals in the blood such as calcium and magnesium.

If all outside causes are eliminated, tests are carried out to identify any disturbances in the brain which include CT (Computerised Axial Tomography) and MRI (Magnetic Resonance Imaging) scans. If there is still no apparent cause, an EEG (Electroencephalogram) will be carried out to identify where the disturbance is coming from in the brain.

Medication

Different types of medication control different types of epilepsy. Sodium Valproate is the most commonly used AED (anti-epileptic drug) as it covers the widest spectrum of seizure types, while having the least side-effects. All medication has some side effects, however, and these vary depending on the medication. For instance Sodium Valproate (brand name Epilim) is known to cause weight gain and tremors.

> ❝ It's important to note that some medications can affect the child's behaviour and ability to concentrate, so any problem areas should be highlighted as early as possible to aid normal progression. ❞

It's important to note that some medications can affect the child's behaviour and ability to concentrate, so any problem areas should be highlighted as early as possible to aid normal progression.

Most medications are available in flavoured suspensions to make administering them easier. Those that only come in tablet form, such as Topiramate (brand name Topamax), may need to be cut for correct dosage, and crushed for administration.

Most of the time physicians try to prescribe drugs to be taken in the morning and evening, so it's unlikely that you will have to administer these. If you do, however, it is important to have everything well documented and agreed with the parents of the child (please see the Individual Care Plan and Seizure Chart at the back of this booklet).

Only 52% of people with epilepsy are fit-free, though 70% could be with the right treatment.

Alternative Therapies

Not all children respond well to medication, so they may undergo other treatments which you will need to be aware of.

The ketogenic diet

Fasting produces ketones, which are known to control seizure activity. The diet works by tricking the body into believing that it is starving, thus producing ketones. This is done by eating a diet high in fat and low in carbohydrates. When fat is eaten without enough carbohydrate to help 'burn' it, the resulting 'ash' contains ketones.

The diet has to be prescribed by the child's physician and monitored by a specialist dietician. It's very strict and can't be altered at all. It's so sensitive that even one sweet could cause the child to have a seizure.

The parents of children on this diet should provide you with the necessary food and liquids to help maintain it.

It's important to respect any treatment that parents feel is of benefit to their child, and to carry out what is laid down in the ICP.

Paediatric osteopathy

It is possible that as a nanny or au pair, you will be asked to take your child for osteopathic treatment. Osteopathy is a natural, non-invasive way of treating many illnesses and disorders, from colic to cerebral palsy. It treats the body as a whole, interconnected structure and works by relieving tension in the skeletal system and, therefore, any effects this may be having elsewhere in the body.

In epilepsy, cranial osteopathy can be effective, as this focuses on the skull and spine, alleviating tension and allowing the spinal fluid to drain and flow more freely.

Homeopathy

Homeopathic remedies, used for many ailments, have such well-documented proof of their efficacy that treatment is now available on the NHS. As with normal medication, any

❝ It's important to respect any treatment that parents feel is of benefit to their child, and to carry out what is laid down in the ICP. ❞

compounds that you are asked to give your child should be documented and agreed in the individual care plan (ICP).

Aromatherapy

Research carried out by Dr Tim Betts of the Queen Elizabeth Hospital, Birmingham, suggests that aromatherapy can help to control epilepsy in some cases. People whose seizures begin with a warning (such as a funny taste in the mouth or the twitching of one limb) can breathe in the aroma of oils such as lavender and ylang ylang in order to relax, which then stops or reduces the severity of their seizure.

Emergency Treatments

Generalised seizures are potentially much more dangerous than partial seizures. They affect the whole brain, which results in a loss of consciousness and can cause injury due to a fall. If the seizure lasts longer than five minutes, it can also cause damage to the brain.

It is, therefore, vitally important that staff know what to do in the case of an emergency. Please refer to, and copy, the emergency procedure page opposite.

It should be noted that staff are under no legal obligation to administer medication, so the wishes of both staff and parents should be made clear in the ICP.

There are currently two main emergency treatments that can be administered if a child has a prolonged seizure. These are *rectal diazepam* and *buccal medazolam*.

Rectal diazepam is a ready prepared solution that is administered as the name suggests: rectally. *Buccal medazolam* comes as liquid drops that should be placed inside the child's cheek. Due to child protection issues with the administration of rectal diazepam, buccal medazolam is now more frequently prescribed.

Emergency treatments should be thoroughly outlined, so as to avoid any confusion. The parents should sign a consent form for all medicines to be administered, and this is included in the ICP.

> **It should be noted that staff are under no legal obligation to administer medication, so the wishes of both staff and parents should be made clear in the ICP.**

If staff are willing to administer rectal diazepam in an emergency, training can be arranged through the National Society for Epilepsy (contact details at rear of booklet).

The recovery position

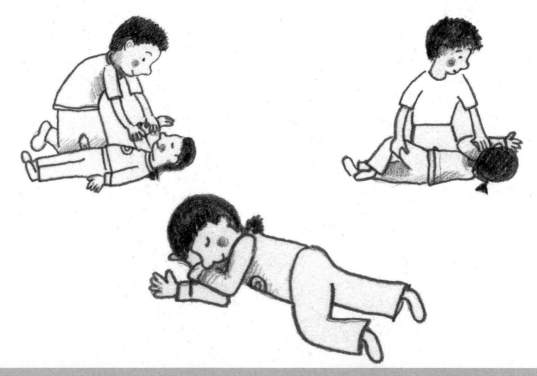

Aid the child breathing by gently placing him in the recovery position, above, once the seizure is finished

Emergency procedure for generalised Epilepsy seizures

- stay calm;

- ensure that the child is in a safe place, away from any objects that may cause harm;

- quietly remove other children from the area, so as to avoid embarrassment in case of incontinence;

- do not restrain the child or put anything in his mouth;

- time the length of the seizure;

- call an ambulance if the seizure lasts more than five minutes, or two minutes longer than normal;

- depending on the child's care plan, administer emergency medication with at least one same-sex witness as the child;

- once the child has stopped fitting, roll him into the recovery position;

- let the child rest for as long as he needs;

- only give food or liquids when the child is fully conscious again.

Learning Implications

Most children with epilepsy have no problems with learning, but others may have difficulty due to:

- **poor concentration**
- **memory loss**
- **inappropriate behaviour**
- **language and communication problems**
- **motor skill reduction.**

The main causes are seizures themselves, side effects from medication and psychological factors.

Seizures

Parts of lessons may be missed and concentration can be impaired. The more frequent the seizures, the greater the impact.

If the focus of the child's seizures is in the temporal lobe of the brain, memory and therefore learning will be affected.

Anti-epileptic medication

Some anti-epilepsy drugs (AEDs) can cause drowsiness. This can affect concentration, memory and response time.

Some behavioural problems have been associated with AEDs, such as Topiramate which can cause an increase in aggression.

Psychological factors

These include attitudes towards the child and his condition, as well as his own self-image.

As some children with epilepsy have to be excluded from certain activities, they may come to resent their condition and feel alienated from their peers.

Problem areas can be identified and addressed with the aid of your area SENCO (special educational needs co-ordinator).

Activities

Most children with epilepsy can join in normal activities, but there are some which may be dangerous for them. Again, working with the child's parents is important in identifying any activities which they feel may be unsuitable for their child.

Cycling

Any child should be well protected with a hat and pads when cycling and this is especially important for epileptic children. It is potentially very dangerous if a child fits whilst riding a bike, so care should be taken to supervise him at all times, and never to let him ride on the road.

Swimming

As long as the child is supervised, swimming is a very safe and enjoyable activity. The life guard should be made aware of the child's condition, and if there is a high risk of seizure activity, it may be advisable to clothe the child in an easily noticeable garment such as a red t-shirt.

If the child fits while in the water, you should gently hold his head out of the water until the seizure has passed before taking him out of the pool.

Climbing

The obvious risk of a fall suggests that great care should be taken if the child is climbing. If the child fits frequently, it should be discussed with the parents to determine if climbing should be allowed.

Other Activities

Team activities such as football should be encouraged as they are both safe and help the child to feel more 'normal'.

It's very important for their self-esteem that children with epilepsy are not made to feel different from their peers, and are included in as many activities as possible.

If a child fits frequently and cannot join in some activities, he should be allowed to choose another activity instead to avoid feelings of frustration and resentment of his condition, though he should never be allowed to use it as an excuse or be given special treatment because of it.

Drawing, painting and other creative play can be good ways for the child to express himself. A colouring activity to copy and use is included in the back of this booklet. It can also be used as a learning aid if you are teaching young children about epilepsy.

Case Study

Sandra has been caring for Daniel, three, since he developed epilepsy. I asked Sandra to describe looking after Daniel.

"When I first started looking after Daniel he would fit quite often. I think this was because they had to change his medication a lot until they found the right one. He used to have a few different seizure types; tonic-clonic, absence, atonic and myoclonic seizures. I would write down what happened, when they happened, how long they lasted, and if Daniel was hurt in any way.

Danny's mother went through the emergency procedure, which was mainly for his tonic-clonic seizures, and I have a chart that I can refer to. In the beginning, I would have to give Daniel some medication at lunch time, so his Mum and I made up a consent form which included the amount and time that the medicine should be given. It was easy to give him the medicine as it was in a sugary solution.

I was shocked when I first saw Daniel have a tonic-clonic seizure, but his mother was with us so she reassured me and talked me through it. There was no warning when Daniel suddenly fell to the floor and started to make jerking movements. It was alarming because he turned a bit blue in the face as his breathing was restricted during the seizure. It lasted just over a minute and then stopped just as suddenly as it started. Daniel's breathing returned to normal and he slept for about half an hour afterwards.

As Daniel is still young, it's difficult to see if his epilepsy is affecting his learning, but he loves drawing and singing nursery rhymes. He also loves the outdoors, and particularly enjoys playing football. He has a soft protective hat that he can wear if he wants to go on the slide or climbing frame. He doesn't fit so much anymore, but I still watch him closely all the time, just in case.

Daniel is a really affectionate little boy, and has a great personality. It can be quite hard to keep up with him sometimes though! I have learnt a lot about epilepsy since I have been looking after him and it's been great to be able to watch his progress as his condition has improved."

Sandra Green.

Famous people with epilepsy

Actors

Name	Life	Comments
Bud Abbott	(1897–1974)	Of Abbott and Costello. He had epilepsy all his life.
Ward Bond	(1903–1960)	A film actor whose epilepsy meant that he was rejected from the draft for World War II.
Danny Glover	(1946—)	An actor and film director who had epilepsy from age 15 to age 35.
Margaux Hemingway	(1955–1996)	A film actress and model who had epilepsy from the age of 7.
Martin Kemp	(1961—)	Actor and former bassist with the pop band Spandau Ballet who has had epilepsy since having two brain tumours in the 1990s.
Rik Mayall	(1958—)	A comedian and actor who was seriously injured and put in a coma for five days after a quad bike accident in 1998.
Hugo Weaving	(1960—)	An actor who has taken anticonvulsants for epilepsy since his first seizure when he was 13.

Musicians

Name	Life	Comments
Jimmy Reed	(1925–1976)	An American blues singer.
Neil Young	(1945—)	Singer-songwriter.
Lindsey Buckingham	(1949—)	Guitarist and singer in the music group Fleetwood Mac. He was taken to hospital after a seizure while on tour, aged 29.
Ian Curtis	(1956–1980)	The vocalist and lyricist of the band Joy Division was diagnosed with epilepsy aged 22. The cover of their album Unknown Pleasures resembles an EEG tracing, but is actually the tracings of the radio emissions of a pulsar.
Richard Jobson	(1960—)	Formerly the lead singer with the punk rock group, The Skids, now a television presenter and film maker. He has absence seizures.
Edith Bowman	(1975—)	Scottish television presenter and radio DJ, who had epilepsy as a child.
Adam Horovitz	(1966—)	Member of the music group Beastie Boys.
Mike Skinner	(1978—)	Also known as The Streets, he had epilepsy between the ages of 7 and 20.

Sport

Name	Life	Comments
Tony Greig	(1946—)	A former cricketer and commentator who is involved with Epilepsy Action Australia. He had his first seizure, aged 14, during a tennis game.
Maggie McEleny	(1965—)	Four times British Paralympic swimmer, winning 3 gold, 5 silver and 7 bronze medals. McEleny has paraplegia and epilepsy. In 2000, she was made an MBE and awarded a Golden Jubilee Award by the British Epilepsy Association.

Jonty Rhodes	(1969—)	A cricketer who is involved with Epilepsy South Africa.
Tom Smith	(1971—)	Former Scottish international and Northampton Saints rugby player. Has had epilepsy since the age of 18. His seizures occur only at night, during sleep. He is a patron of the Scottish epilepsy charity Enlighten.

Art and writing

Edward Lear	(1812–1888)	An artist, illustrator and writer known for his nonsensical poetry and limericks. His epilepsy, which he developed as a child, may have been inherited (his elder sister Jane had frequent seizures and died young). Lear was ashamed of his epilepsy and kept it a secret. He did, however, record each seizure in his diary.
Fyodor Dostoyevsky	(1821–1881)	A Russian writer whose epilepsy was probably inherited (both his father and his son had seizures). He incorporated his experiences into his novels – creating four different characters with epilepsy. Dostoyevsky's epilepsy was unusual in that he claimed to experience an ecstatic aura prior to a seizure, whereas most people experience unpleasant feelings.
R. D. Blackmore	(1825–1900)	Author of Lorna Doone.
Laurie Lee	(1914–1997)	A poet, novelist and screenwriter, most famous for Cider with Rosie. His epilepsy probably developed after he was knocked down by a bicycle at the age of 10. He kept it secret and it only surfaced when his papers were read by biographers after his death.
Max Clifford	(1943—)	A publicist known for representing controversial clients. He developed epilepsy at the age of 46.

Miscellaneous

Socrates	(470–399 BC)	Ancient Greek philosopher. It is speculated that his daimonion was a simple partial seizure and that he had temporal lobe epilepsy.
Julius Caesar	(100–44 BC)	Roman military and political leader. He had four documented episodes of what where probably complex partial seizures. He may additionally have had absence seizures in his youth. There is family history of epilepsy amongst his ancestors and descendants. The earliest accounts of these seizures were made by the biographer Suetonius who was born after Caesar's death.
Joan of Arc	(1412–1431)	Experienced religious messages through voices and visions which she said others could sometimes experience simultaneously. Some researchers consider the visions to be ecstatic epileptic auras, though more recent research may implicate idiopathic partial epilepsy with auditory features. Epileptic seizures with clear auditory and visual hallucinations are very rare. This, together with the extreme length of her visions, lead some to reject epilepsy as a cause.

Quick guide to seizures

Tonic-clonic seizure

Consciousness is lost from the beginning of the seizure. The child will go stiff (tonic phase), then fall to the ground. His muscles will then begin to rapidly tighten and relax, creating a jerking motion (clonic phase).

Absence seizure

Literally an absence or lapse in awareness which is characterised by a blank stare lasting just a few seconds. The child's eyes may blink quickly or roll upwards which can be accompanied by chewing movements of the mouth. The child will be unaware of his surroundings, but will quickly recover.

Myoclonic

'Myo' means muscle, and these seizures involve sudden, brief, muscle jerks that include parts or all of the body.

Atonic

'Atonic' means without tone, and seizures of this type cause a temporary loss of all muscle control, which results in a sudden collapse and fall to the ground.

Simple partial seizure

The specific area of the brain where the seizure begins determines what the seizure will look or feel like. Jerking may begin in one part of the body and proceed to another. A simple partial seizure may spread to the rest of the brain and is then known as a secondary generalised seizure.

Complex partial seizure

This usually begins with a blank stare, often followed by chewing and random repetitive activities. The child will have no recollection of what happened during the seizure.

Status epilepticus

This is the name given to the state of constant seizure, when either one seizure doesn't stop, or one follows another without time to recover in between.

Postictal period

This is the period following a seizure and varies depending on the type, duration and intensity of the seizure. Most children will feel tired and may suffer from muscle soreness, headache, and pain in the tongue or cheek if they were bitten. The child will probably be confused and will need to rest.

Seizure chart

Child's name:..

DoB:...

Type of seizure (if known):..

Time seizure occurred:...

How long did it last?...

What was the child doing when the seizure occurred?...

....

....

....

Was there any warning?..

Did the child lose consciousness?...

What colour was the child's face?..

What part of the child's body moved during the seizure?..

....

Was the child hurt?..

Did the child become incontinent?..

How was the child after the seizure?...

....

Details of any action taken:..

....

....

Details of any medication given:...

....

Seizure witnessed by...

Form completed by...Date:....................

Individual care plan for children with epilepsy

Name:..

Address:..

DoB::..

School:..

....

Headteacher:...

Staff trained to administer medication:..

....

....

Emergency contact no:...

Type of epilepsy:...

Seizure/s experienced:...

....

Description:...

....

....

Possible pattern or trigger:..

....

Procedure following seizure:..

....

Medication prescribed:..

....

Colour me in!

The Latin for seahorse is hippocampus, and in the brain the hippocampus is often the focal point of epileptic activity.

Useful Contacts

The National Society for Epilepsy
Telephone: 01494 601 305
Email: training@epilepsynse.org.uk
Website: www.epilepsynse.org.uk

Epilepsy Action
Telephone: 0808 800 5050
Website: www.epilepsy.org.uk

National Centre for Young People with Epilepsy
Telephone: 01342 832 243
www.ncype.org.uk

Epilepsy Therapy Development Project
www.epilepsy.com

Epilepsy Information
www.epilepsyinfo.co.uk

Epilepsy Research UK
www.epilepsyresearch.org.uk

Real Time Health
(offers educational real time videos)
www.realtimehealth.com

All these websites were accessed in August 2007.